Contents

Any words appearing in the text in bold, **like this**, are explained in the Glossary.

The diabetes epidemic

Diabetes is much more common than it was twenty years ago. By 2010, it will affect about 220 million people around the world. It is turning into a big problem for healthcare providers.

People with diabetes have too much **glucose** in their bloodstream. Glucose is a type of sugar in food that everyone needs for energy. People with diabetes cannot convert it properly into energy because their bodies cannot make or cannot use a key substance, **insulin**.

Insulin is a **hormone** made in a **gland** called the **pancreas**, a banana-sized organ that lies across the back of the stomach. It helps glucose to get into **cells** where it can be broken down for energy or stored.

Types of diabetes

There are two types of diabetes: type 1 and type 2. Type 1 diabetes is most common in young people. At an early age, their pancreas stops making insulin.

You cannot feel your pancreas through your skin. Doctors use scanners to look at it.

Liver

Stomach

Pancreas

Intestines

Type 2 diabetes used to occur only in middle-aged and elderly people. But it is now starting to affect people in their 20s and 30s, and even some teenagers. The pancreas still makes some insulin, but their body does not use it properly. So glucose levels build up in the blood, instead of being broken down and turned into energy.

The main reason that type 2 diabetes is growing more common is that many people are becoming overweight. A big effort is needed to change the way people look after themselves.

The cost of diabetes

Both type 1 and type 2 diabetes can be treated with diet and drugs. But having too much glucose in the blood for a long time gradually damages important parts of the body, including **blood vessels** and **nerves.**

Diabetes not only makes people ill, it costs countries a lot of money. Some people with diabetes need expensive treatment and have to stay in hospital. This is why governments need to do something about the diabetes **epidemic.**

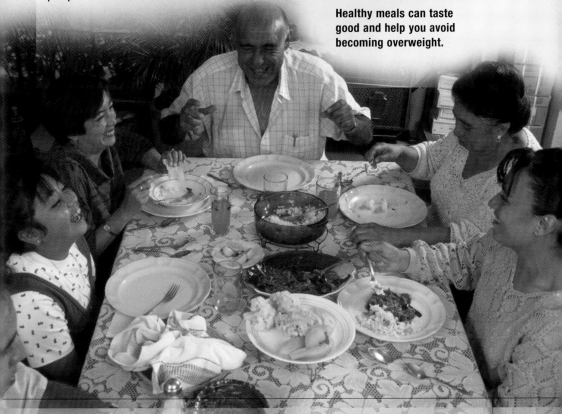

Healthy meals can taste good and help you avoid becoming overweight.

The history of diabetes

Egyptian doctors described diabetes as early as 1500 BCE, according to an ancient piece of papyrus found in Luxor, Upper Egypt, in 1872. They also had a treatment for it that included beer swill, cucumber flower and pond water.

But it was not until about 250 BCE that Apollonius of Memphis, Egypt is thought to have named the disease 'diabetes'. Meaning 'to go through', the name shows that physicians understood that people with the disease were getting rid of more fluid than they could drink. Great thirst and a need to pass a lot of **urine** are two of the common symptoms of diabetes.

In 500 CE, two Indian doctors, Susruta and Charuka, reported the sweet, sugary urine produced by people with diabetes. It was sweet because of the **glucose** in it. But the disease did not get its full name – *diabetes mellitus* – until later, in Roman times. 'Mellitus' is the Latin word for honey, which is clearly very sweet.

Early treatments

Over the next 900 years, physicians treated people with diabetes with some extraordinary treatments, including herbs and bleeding. To bleed a person, a doctor cut the patient or used leeches to draw out the blood.

At one point, Greek physicians prescribed exercise, preferably on horseback, to reduce patients' need to pass urine. As late as the 17th century, a leading medical text suggested powdered mouse (with fleas) for treating diabetes!

Removing blood from a vein used to be a common treatment.

Famous people who have or had diabetes

- Novelist H G Wells (1866–1946), author of *The Time Machine, The Invisible Man* and other books
- Menachem Begin, Prime Minister of Israel (1913–83)
- US country musician, Johnny Cash (1932–)
- American jazz singer, Ella Fitzgerald (1917–96)
- French impressionist painter, Paul Cézanne (1839–1906)
- American industrialist, Howard Hughes (1905–76)
- Pakistani cricketer, Wasim Akram (1966–)
- US tennis player, Arthur Ashe (1943–93)
- US boxer, Sugar Ray Robinson (1929–89)
- British Olympic rower, Sir Steve Redgrave (1962–)
- American actress, Halle Berry (1968–)

Sugar Ray Robinson, an American professional boxer who was six times a world champion.

The pancreas

With so much emphasis on the sweet urine of people with diabetes, doctors not unreasonably assumed it was a disease of the **kidneys** – the organs in the body that clean the blood and produce urine. It was not until late in the 18th century that researchers discovered that the blood of people with diabetes was also sugary. They rightly concluded that diabetes was a disease that affected the whole body.

In 1869 an **anatomist**, called Paul Langerhans, identified the key **cells** in the pancreas – the **islets of Langerhans** – which are now known to produce the main substance that controls glucose levels in the body. Twenty years later, two German researchers made the connection between the **pancreas** and diabetes. When they removed the pancreas of some dogs, the animals went on to develop diabetes.

The history of diabetes

The discovery of insulin

Once they realized that the islets of Langerhans were the key to diabetes, early 20th-century researchers set about extracting the key ingredient – **insulin** – that controls glucose levels in the body. However, they soon found that this was much more difficult than they had expected.

The pancreas does not just make insulin, it also makes **enzymes** to digest food in the intestines. At first, scientists couldn't extract insulin without these enzymes. As soon as the mixture was in a test tube, the enzymes digested the insulin.

Banting and Best

In October 1920, a Canadian doctor called Frederick Banting came up with the idea of tying off parts of the pancreas in order to kill the cells that produced **digestive enzymes**, without damaging the islets of Langerhans.

Working with a colleague, Charles Best, Banting gradually improved his technique for extracting insulin from the pancreas. The pair tested their insulin on dogs with diabetes and found they were able to control the animals' glucose levels. Realizing the importance of the research, other scientists at the University of Toronto joined Banting and Best in extracting and purifying the insulin.

Dramatic results

In early 1922, the first patient with diabetes was injected with a small amount of insulin. Leonard Thompson was 14 years old. Until then, he had been kept alive by the 'starvation diet' used to treat people with diabetes at that time. As a result, he weighed only about 30 kg when he was treated with Banting and Best's new pancreatic extract.

The first injection had only a small effect. But when Leonard was re-injected with a purer extract of insulin some weeks later, the results were dramatic. The amount of glucose in his blood fell and he soon started to gain weight and strength. Other patients were treated with increasingly refined samples of insulin with similar good results.

Without Banting (right) and Best (left), people might have had to wait longer for effective treatments for diabetes.

A prize-winning achievement

Within a few years, insulin became widely available. In 1923, Banting was awarded the Nobel Prize for Medicine, an important international award, because his research was considered so important. In 1934, he was given the title 'Sir'. Seven years later, however, he was killed in an air crash in Newfoundland.

After insulin

Before the discovery of insulin, a child with type 1 diabetes would live only a few weeks. A middle-aged adult diagnosed with type 2 diabetes would die within 10 years. By 1945, when insulin was widely available, there had been a big improvement. A newly diagnosed 10-year-old could expect to live until about 45 or 50, and a 50-year-old until he or she was about 65. Today, people with diabetes still live five to ten fewer years than people who do not have the condition. But they lead much healthier and more normal lives than those who had diabetes 100 or even 50 years ago.

After the initial successes with insulin, researchers found ways to make a dose of treatment work for longer in the body, so that people with diabetes did not need to inject themselves so often.

Making insulin in a factory in 1946. The purified insulin flows out at the bottom into the bucket.

Genetic engineering

Until the 1970s, people injected themselves with insulin taken from the pancreas of cattle or pigs. Then came a big breakthrough for many modern insulin users, when scientists found a way to produce human insulin by **genetic engineering**. This involves putting the **gene** that controls normal insulin production in the human pancreas into bacterial cells. The gene is 'switched on' so that the **bacteria** make insulin. Some people still find that they respond better to animal insulin. But the genetically engineered human insulin is better for many.

New treatments

There were also new treatments for people with type 2 diabetes, starting with drugs called **sulphonylureas** in the 1950s. In the second half of the 20th century, the differences between type 1 and type 2 diabetes became clearer.

For example, researchers called type 1 diabetes an auto-immune disease. This is a disease in which the cells that normally defend the body from infection start to attack other cells in the body. In type 1 diabetes, these cells attack the islets of Langerhans.

By finding out more about the causes of type 1 and type 2 diabetes, scientists were able to tailor treatment more accurately to the different types of diabetes.

Good glucose control

In 1993, doctors discovered that people with type 1 diabetes who kept the amount of glucose in their blood under really good control had the fewest health problems. By testing their blood regularly and using medication to keep their glucose at near-normal levels, they had fewer complications than people who were less careful. Their heart and other organs, **blood vessels** and **nerves** were in better shape. A further study, published in 1998, confirmed that the same was true for people with type 2 diabetes.

As a result of this research, people with diabetes are encouraged to check their **blood-glucose levels** regularly and adapt their treatment according to the results.

Type 1 diabetes

Type 1 diabetes is sometimes called **insulin**-dependent diabetes or juvenile-onset diabetes. It occurs when a person's body cannot make the **hormone** insulin.

Insulin helps to convert **glucose** into energy in **cells** all over the body. The body gets its glucose by digesting starchy, carbohydrate foods in the diet, such as bread, potatoes, pasta and rice. The glucose in these foods is absorbed from the intestine into the bloodstream.

During a meal, the **pancreas** makes insulin. It is then released into the bloodstream where it helps glucose get out of the blood and into cells. Once the glucose is inside the cells it acts as fuel to provide the body with energy or it is sent for storage in muscle and liver cells.

Symptoms of diabetes

Without insulin, people with type 1 diabetes are unable to use the **carbohydrates** and sugar in their food properly. They start feeling very unwell. Some of the symptoms they get occur with other illnesses too. It is when several symptoms are all present at once that it could be diabetes.

A very common symptom of diabetes is feeling thirsty – not just after playing sport or when it is hot – but all the time. People need to drink a lot, and then they need to pass **urine** frequently too.

Another symptom is feeling very tired. This is because people with diabetes cannot get enough energy from the glucose in their food. It is not just the tiredness people feel after a busy day. They feel tired nearly all the time, even after a good night's sleep or without doing anything very active.

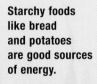

Starchy foods like bread and potatoes are good sources of energy.

12

Diabetes also makes people lose weight, as they do not get enough nourishment from their food. It is not like the effects of dieting. They seem to be eating enough but they just get thinner.

Infections

A lot of glucose in the bloodstream can lead to fungal infection. There are many different types of fungi, not just mushrooms and toadstools. One type of fungal infection, called thrush, looks a bit like cottage cheese. In people who are ill, including those with diabetes, it can grow in many different parts of the body, including a woman's vagina or a man's penis, or sometimes in the mouth.

"I'd had the typical diabetes symptoms – hunger, thirst, weight loss, fatigue and going to the bathroom as though it was my new best friend. I remember my mum carting me off to the local doctor and having a urine and blood test done. I really had no idea what was going on. When the doctor told me I had diabetes I didn't really think it was such a big deal because I'd never even heard of it until that day!"

(Dani from Australia, age 14, from www.childrenwithdiabetes.com)

13

Type 2 diabetes

Type 2 diabetes tends to develop more slowly than type 1 diabetes. The **cells** in the **islets of Langerhans** that make **insulin** do not suddenly fail. Instead, they gradually deteriorate, and the body does not respond properly to the insulin that the Islet cells make.

Insulin resistance

Cells, particularly in the muscles, liver and fat develop **insulin resistance**. They can no longer use insulin to get **glucose** into their cells, so glucose levels rise in the bloodstream. The islets of Langerhans try to make up for this by producing more insulin. For a while, there are higher than average levels of the **hormone** in the blood. But eventually, the islet cells get worn out and produce less and less insulin.

Rise in type 2 diabetes

At one time, type 2 diabetes was called 'maturity-onset' diabetes since it only started (the onset) in middle aged and elderly (mature) people.

"Television viewing is thought to promote weight gain not only by displacing physical activity, but also by increasing energy intake ... US and British children are exposed to about ten food commercials per hour of television time ... most for fast food, soft drinks, sweets, and sugar-sweetened breakfast cereal."

(Cara B Ebbeling, Dorota B Pawlak, David S Ludwig, *The Lancet*, 2002)

But it is now affecting much younger people, including teenagers and young adults.

Type 2 diabetes is sometimes called 'mild' diabetes. But it is just as serious as type 1 diabetes. The symptoms are similar to those of type 1 diabetes, but they may build up more slowly. The long-term damage to **blood vessels, nerves**, eyes and major organs can be just as serious as with type 1 diabetes.

Diabetes specialists are very concerned at the rise in type 2 diabetes in younger people. They are linking it to the big increase in the number of teenagers and young adults who are overweight or **obese**.

Diet and exercise

Young people eat more sweet and fatty foods than their parents and grandparents did at their age. There are many more of these foods to choose from, especially snack foods like burgers, crisps, biscuits and sweets, and there are more places to buy them.

Children and teenagers also get less exercise than previous generations. Far fewer walk to school and they play less sport. Instead, they tend to relax by hanging out with their friends, watching TV or playing computer games. All this means that they use up less energy and more of the food they eat is converted into fat.

It's fine for these young people to relax, as long as they exercise and eat sensibly, too.

Type 2 diabetes

IGT

Before people develop type 2 diabetes, they usually go through a phase when their body does not handle glucose as efficiently as it should. They do not have diabetes yet, but they are starting to show signs of insulin resistance. This phase is called impaired glucose tolerance (IGT), or 'pre-diabetes'.

People with IGT do not need the same treatment as those with diabetes. But they can take steps to reduce their risk of going on to develop the disease. Many are overweight and eat too many sweet and fatty foods. They might not take enough exercise.

No symptoms

People with impaired glucose tolerance do not usually have any symptoms, so they are unlikely to go to their doctor for help. But a growing number of diabetes specialists support the idea of national **screening** programmes to test the **blood-glucose levels** of people who are at high risk of IGT.

People with close relatives with diabetes are more likely to have IGT than those who do not have a family history. People who are overweight or have high blood pressure or other signs of heart disease are also more likely to have IGT.

"We are now in the process of changing the public health message to say to doctors they not only need to do a better job caring for diabetes, but they have to find people at high risk and they need to do something about the onset of diabetes. That is a ... lot to ask a doctor or a nurse to do."

(Frank Vinicor, diabetes program director for the US Centers for Disease Control and Prevention, *Philadelphia Inquirer*, 12 August 2002)

If all these people were invited to go to special clinics for blood tests, doctors could find out if they had IGT. Blood-glucose levels in people with IGT are not as high as in those with diabetes, but they are higher than normal. Finding out they had IGT would give people time to change their diet, lose weight, take more exercise and reduce their risk before they developed diabetes.

Setting up and running this type of clinic costs a lot of money, so there are not many of these screening programmes. Most people do not realize they have a problem until they are found to have diabetes.

Playing sports can help control your weight and help you avoid IGT and diabetes.

The rise of diabetes

The continuing rise of diabetes in both developed and developing countries appears unstoppable. In 1985, it was estimated that about 30 million people around the world had diabetes. By 2000, only 15 years later, the figure had risen to over 150 million. The World Health Organization predicts that by 2025, the number of people with diabetes will have almost doubled, to about 300 million.

Spending the day at a desk doesn't use much energy. Lack of exercise can lead to a weight problem and diabetes.

The largest increase is likely to be in developing countries in Africa and South-east Asia rather than in developed regions, such as the USA, Europe and Australasia. The big rise in diabetes has been in type 2, not type 1 diabetes, and 9 out of 10 cases of diabetes are now type 2.

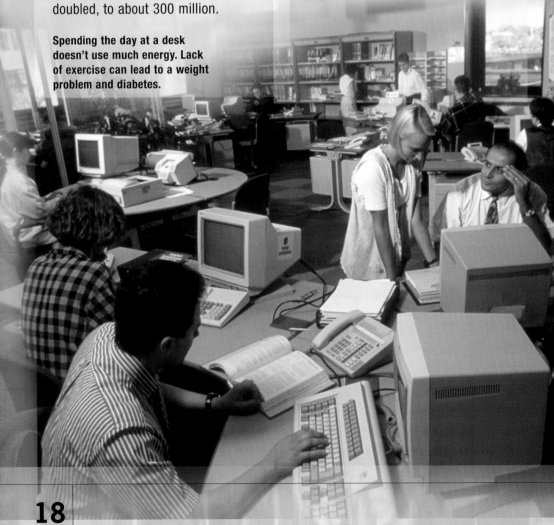

There are two main reasons for the alarming increase in diabetes:

- More people are living longer and reaching an age at which the risk of type 2 diabetes increases.
- Many people eat too much, especially sweet and fatty 'fast' or 'junk' foods. They are also less active. This means that more people are becoming overweight and **obese**, and are increasing their risk of developing type 2 diabetes.

Urbanization

All over the world, lifestyles are changing and a lot of people have different diets from their parents and grandparents. Many are moving to cities in search of work. They may spend all day sitting in offices whereas once they might have worked the land. Some people snack throughout the day, at their desk, in the shopping mall, or in the car, instead of sitting down to regular meals at home. Diabetes tends to be an urban disease and, as urbanization spreads across the globe, diabetes is moving with it.

Worldwide diabetes statistics

In 2000, the five countries with the largest numbers of people with diabetes were:

- India 32.7 million (population 1,008 million)
- China 22.6 million (population 1,275 million)
- United States 15.3 million (population 283 million)
- Pakistan 8.8 million (population 141 million)
- Japan 7.1 million (population 127 million).

Europe has 26.5 million people with diabetes and Australasia has 1 million.

The five countries with the highest rates of the disease were Papua New Guinea (15.5%), Mauritius (15.0%), Bahrain (14.8%), Mexico (14.2%) and Trinidad & Tobago (14.1%).

(International Diabetes Federation; population figures from United Nations Population Division)

Cultural factors

Some **ethnic groups** are more likely to develop diabetes – especially type 2 diabetes – than others. Amongst them are African Americans, African Caribbeans, Native Americans and South Asian people. For example, in the USA, African Americans are twice as likely to have diabetes as non-Hispanic whites, and a quarter of African Americans between the ages of 65 and 74 have diabetes.

The ethnic groups that are most likely to have diabetes may have **genes** that increase their risk, but no one is sure what the genes are. Economic factors could be important too. Groups with relatively high levels of poverty, such as African Americans in the USA, tend to eat a poor diet and have more health problems than better-off groups.

Informing people

Changing their diet to reduce the amount of sweet and fatty foods that they eat, taking more exercise, and taking better care of their health can all help reduce a person's risk of developing diabetes, whatever their cultural origins.

Native Americans have a high risk of diabetes. Exercise reduces the risk.

But some people may not realize how important these things are, especially if they do not speak or cannot read the language of the country in which they are living. They may not be able to afford to see healthcare workers who can test them for diabetes and explain how to treat the condition. They may miss out on regular check-ups for complications.

Simply translating information sheets into languages that people can understand is not enough. Getting across the message about the importance of a healthy lifestyle and effective diabetes treatment involves more than that. People need to trust the doctor or nurse who is trying to help them before they will accept their advice. This takes time and commitment from everyone – patients, their families and healthcare workers.

Fasting

Doctors advise people with diabetes who want to observe religious festivals involving fasting, such as Ramadan, to seek medical advice before they start. During Ramadan, Muslims do not eat anything from sunrise to sunset. But this can be difficult for people with diabetes.

They will need to change the dose of their medication and, if they have problems with their **blood-glucose levels**, they may need to stop fasting. Religious leaders are very understanding of the health needs of people with certain conditions, such as diabetes, for whom fasting may be dangerous. They can advise people how to avoid damaging their health.

Muslims with diabetes can get medical advice about fasting safely in Ramadan.

21

Diabetes in pregnancy

Some women are found to have diabetes when they are pregnant. This is called gestational diabetes. If it happens during the first 12 weeks of the pregnancy, it probably means that a woman had diabetes before she became pregnant. If it starts at a later stage of the pregnancy, it is more likely to be due to the fact that she cannot make enough **insulin** to meet her own needs and that of her baby.

Some women are more likely to develop diabetes during pregnancy than others, such as:
- overweight women
- those with a family history of type 2 diabetes
- women who had a very large baby in a previous pregnancy
- women whose baby died without any clear reason in a previous pregnancy.

Women with gestational diabetes may be able to bring down their **blood-glucose levels** by eating regularly and healthily, and sticking to low-sugar, low-fat foods. But others need insulin to control their blood sugar while they are pregnant.

Eating healthily is especially important during pregnancy. Women with gestational diabetes should take extra care.

Future health problems

Gestational diabetes usually goes away after the baby is born. But women who have had gestational diabetes are three times more likely to develop type 2 diabetes at some time in their life than those who have not had diabetes during pregnancy.

Pregnancy and diabetes among the Pima

The highest levels of diabetes in the world are found in the Pima, a Native American people of Arizona, USA. Over half of the Pima who live on US **reservations** develop type 2 diabetes. They may have **genes** that put them at risk. Also, the Pima tend to be poor, to eat an unhealthy diet and have an inactive lifestyle. This makes things worse.

Recent research has suggested that exposure to high **glucose** levels in the womb also plays a role. Seven out of ten Pima children whose mothers had diabetes when they were pregnant go on to develop diabetes as young adults.

This could be significant for all women with diabetes. Type 2 diabetes used to affect older women who had already had their children. But, as more women get type 2 diabetes when they are young and able to become pregnant, more babies will be exposed to high glucose levels in the womb. This increases their risk of getting diabetes in later life.

A Pima man on a reservation in the USA.

Genetic links

Both type 1 and type 2 diabetes run in families. Often, several people in a family have the condition. Research suggests that they have inherited **genes** from their parents that have made them more likely to get diabetes than other people.

As several genes seem to be involved in diabetes, this makes it hard to work out what is happening. Scientists think that faulty genes on their own are not enough to give people diabetes. Environmental factors are probably at work too. People may inherit genes that increase their risk of getting diabetes. But they may then be exposed to something that changes the way these genes work before they actually develop diabetes.

Diabetes genes

In type 2 diabetes, eating too many sugary and fatty foods and becoming overweight may somehow activate diabetes genes and cause them to develop the condition.

Type 1 diabetes starts much earlier than type 2 diabetes. The genes may be affected by something that a child is exposed to in the first few years of life or even earlier – in the womb, before he or she is born. This could be high **blood-glucose levels** in the mother's bloodstream during pregnancy or it could be exposure to infection at a young age.

Infections

Young children get a lot of minor infections, with no lasting effects. But children with genes for diabetes may respond differently to infection. Their immune system could somehow start to attack the **islets of Langerhans** in their **pancreas**, instead of just protecting them from harmful **microbes**.

Studying twins

Many studies have been done to try to identify the diabetes genes and other possible causes of the condition. Researchers often study identical twins with diabetes in the family because they have exactly the same genes. If it were genes alone that caused diabetes, then either both twins would inherit the genes and develop the condition, or neither twin would inherit the genes and get diabetes. But that does not happen. Often, one twin gets diabetes and the other does not.

So researchers look for differences in the way the children have grown up – different infections they have had, and any differences in diet and lifestyle. They look for anything that may somehow have activated the diabetes genes of one twin, but not the other, and could be a clue to what triggers diabetes in other people too.

An islet of Langerhans (centre). In a healthy pancreas, cells in the islets produce insulin.

cell making insulin

digestive enzymes to intestine

insulin to bloodstream

acini making digestive enzymes

Treating diabetes

Type 1 diabetes

Anyone with type 1 diabetes needs **insulin** injections to replace the **hormone** which they do not make for themselves in their **pancreas**. The aim of treatment is to keep **blood-glucose levels** as well controlled as if the insulin was being produced naturally. This means increasing the amount of insulin in the blood at mealtimes and reducing it between meals.

There are a lot of different brands of insulin and, at present, they all have to be injected. Scientists have never been able to put insulin in a tablet to swallow because it is a **protein**.

The digestive juices in the stomach would break it down before it had a chance to do its job. But they are working on alternative methods of delivery, such as aerosols that allow the insulin to be inhaled.

Genetic engineering

Some people use insulins that are extracted from the pancreases of pigs and cattle, while others use human insulin that is made by **genetic engineering**. In this process, the **gene** which controls normal insulin production in the human pancreas is put into bacterial cells. There, it is 'switched on' so that the **bacteria**

"The pump is not a cure (which is what I would really like) but it has made a lot of things so much easier. I can sleep in on the weekends and I can stay up late with my friends and have late-night snacks! There are even times when I am playing with my friends that I just skip a meal – especially lunch on the weekends, and that's OK too. I don't have to stop what I am doing to have a snack or a meal – I eat what I want when I want."

(Brian from Michigan, USA, age 12, www.childrenwithdiabetes.com)

make human insulin – something that they would not normally do. The insulin is then collected and purified.

Some brands of insulins work fast, while others take longer to 'kick in'. There are types that work only for a few hours, others for much longer. Some people use one type of insulin to control their glucose levels between meals and also take a short-acting insulin at mealtimes. Alternatively, they can use a ready-made insulin mixture which contains some short and some longer-acting insulin.

A once-daily, long-acting brand of insulin is also available that aims to provide steady glucose control throughout the day.

People use insulin pumps to achieve good glucose control without regular injections.

Insulin pumps

Insulin pumps are the high-tech route to better glucose control for many people with type 1 diabetes. Worn on the outside of the body on a belt or in a pocket, the most sophisticated insulin pumps are about the size of a pager. They can be programmed to deliver insulin through a needle inserted under the skin, usually on the **abdomen**.

Between meals the device provides a low level of insulin around the clock. It also allows users to deliver a larger dose before meals, matched to the amount of food they will eat. They can also reduce the amount of insulin they are getting when they exercise, so their blood-glucose levels do not drop too low.

Type 2 diabetes

As people with type 2 diabetes do make some insulin of their own, they do not usually need insulin injections until they have had the illness for some time. Instead, the treatment in the early stages of the condition is aimed at improving the way their body responds to insulin.

Some people at this stage can control their blood-glucose levels by changing their diet and taking more exercise, especially if they are very overweight. Everyone with type 2 diabetes is advised to exercise, and to eat a healthy diet to keep their weight under control – even if they need drugs to treat their diabetes.

Drug treatments

There are several types of drugs for type 2 diabetes and, unlike insulin, they can all be taken as tablets.

Sulphonylureas are the most widely prescribed drugs for type 2 diabetes. They make islet **cells** in the pancreas produce more insulin. Unfortunately, they tend to make people put on weight, which can be a problem for people with type 2 diabetes who are already struggling to keep their weight down.

Metformin is the first choice of treatment for people who are overweight, as it does not make them put on weight. Some doctors prefer it for type 2 diabetes because medical research has shown that it can reduce the risk of complications from diabetes. It lowers blood-glucose levels by reducing the amount of **glucose** released from the liver and by improving the way muscle and fat cells respond to insulin. The downside is that some people get stomach upsets when they take it.

Many people with type 2 diabetes must remember to take several pills every day.

Other drugs for type 2 diabetes are usually taken as an 'add-on' therapy when people with type 2 diabetes cannot control their glucose levels with a sulphonylurea or metformin on its own. Some can be taken just at mealtimes to boost insulin release with food.

Many drugs used to treat type 2 diabetes become less effective when people take them for long periods, because glucose levels rise over time. Some people develop unwanted **side effects** from using them, such as stomach upsets. Eventually, most people with type 2 diabetes will probably need to use insulin in addition to their other drugs.

Emergency!

The most common reason for a diabetic emergency is too little rather than too much sugar in the bloodstream. This is called **hypoglycaemia**, or a 'hypo'.

Hypoglycaemia

Hypoglycaemia usually happens when people with diabetes have more **insulin** in their bloodstream than they need, so their **blood-glucose levels** drop too low. This can happen if they have not eaten as much as they expected or if they have used up more energy than they planned.

The normal **pancreas** adapts to changes in routine. If lunch is late, it waits until there is food in the body before it releases insulin. But people who rely on insulin injections to control their **glucose** levels cannot be so flexible.

❝I play sports like softball and some soccer and when I'm on the field I say 'TIME OUT, I'm low!' Then I drink a juice and eat some crackers and I'm pumped up as ever.❞

(Mallory from Mississippi, USA, www.childrenwithdiabetes.com)

It is important to know how to help a friend with diabetes if she or he has a 'hypo'.

If they are ready to eat, take their insulin or other diabetes medicine, and then get called away and miss the meal, they can have problems. Once the dose of medicine is in their bloodstream, they cannot get it out and their glucose levels may fall too low.

Another common reason for a hypo is when someone uses up more of the glucose in their bloodstream than they had planned by playing sport or going for a long walk.

Having a hypo

When people are having a hypo they can become confused and disoriented. They may slur their speech or become angry and behave strangely. If something is not done to help them, they may fall over and become unconscious. Doctors advise people who experience the first sign of a hypo to drink something sweet and then have a biscuit or snack.

Some people with diabetes buy glucose gels and keep them in their bag. If they have a hypo and are not well enough to swallow, someone can smear the gel on the inside of their mouth. This is a really quick way to get glucose into their bloodstream.

Hypos do not have any lasting effects. After eating or drinking something sweet or using a glucose gel, a person usually feels better within 10 to 15 minutes and can continue as normal.

Taking special care

Having a hypo while driving or handling dangerous machinery is dangerous, so people with diabetes need to take special care to check their blood-glucose levels regularly. They should not miss meals when they are on the road or working with machines.

Although hypos sound very scary, most people get used to recognizing the early warning symptoms and taking action.

Warning! Hypo!

Typical hypo warning signs are:
- feeling panicky, hungry, wobbly or confused
- tingling in the mouth and lips
- blurred eyesight
- sweating
- rapid heartbeat.

Complications

Thanks to modern treatments, few people in the developed world die as a direct result of high **blood-glucose levels**. But they do get complications that affect many parts of their body. Complications of diabetes result from the long-term effects of high blood-glucose levels on the **blood vessels**.

Diabetic retinopathy

Damage to the small blood vessels in the eye, called diabetic retinopathy, is the most frequent single complication of diabetes. It tends to affect people who have had diabetes for many years, especially if they have not controlled their **glucose** levels very successfully. The condition can lead to blindness.

Blocks, leaks and swelling of the tiny blood vessels at the back of the eye can cause permanent damage to the retina. (This is the part of the eye where images are focused before they are sent to the brain.) Diabetes is the leading cause of blindness and poor vision in adults living in developed countries.

Leaky blood vessels in the eye caused by diabetes can damage the retina and lead to blindness. The large red area in the centre of this picture is blood that has leaked inside the eye.

Kidney and nerves

Similar damage to the small blood vessels in the **kidneys** can lead to kidney failure. The kidneys are vital organs that clean the blood, so people with kidney failure need their blood cleaned regularly by **dialysis** machines or require a kidney transplant.

Nerves also need a good blood supply to keep them healthy. If the blood vessels supplying them are affected by diabetes, extensive nerve damage can occur. This can lead to impotence in men – they cannot achieve an erection to have sex.

Often people with diabetes hurt their feet because of nerve damage. In extreme cases their feet or legs become so damaged that they have to be **amputated**. Diabetes is the most common cause of amputation that is not the result of an accident. People with diabetes are 15 to 40 times more likely to require a leg amputation compared to the population in general, although it is still uncommon.

Other complications

When high blood-glucose levels damage large blood vessels, this can lead to heart attacks or strokes, which may be fatal. Half of people with diabetes die as a result of heart disease, compared with about 20 per cent of the general population.

In people with type 2 diabetes, complications start surprisingly early, often years before they even know they have the disease. This is why it is so important to diagnose and treat type 2 diabetes as early as possible.

People with kidney failure need a dialysis machine to keep their blood clean.

Preventing type 2 diabetes

Diet and exercise

Diet and exercise have been shown to delay and possibly prevent people at high risk of getting type 2 diabetes from developing the condition. In 2001, results from a large US study confirmed what diabetes specialists have thought for some time. Even if a person is overweight and **blood-glucose levels** are starting to go up, it may not be too late to avoid diabetes.

The Diabetes Prevention Programme

Over 3000 people took part in the Diabetes Prevention Programme, sponsored by the National Institute of Diabetes and Digestive and **Kidney** Diseases, in the USA. They were as young as 25 and as old as 85. They were black, white, Asian and Hispanic Americans. Some had a family history of diabetes, and some of the women had had diabetes when they were pregnant. What they all had in common was that they were overweight and they had impaired glucose tolerance (see pages 16–17).

The cost of diabetes

The complications of diabetes, such as blindness, kidney failure and heart disease, cost healthcare services a huge amount of money. Diabetes costs an estimated 5–10 per cent of a nation's health budget.

A third of the group went on the lifestyle programme, a third took **metformin** (see page 29) to reduce their **glucose** levels, and a third did nothing (though they were given information about diet and exercise, as were those who took metformin). Those who took part in the lifestyle programme were given special training about healthy eating and encouraged to exercise for 30 minutes each day. Most chose walking.

Results of the programme

After three years, those who went on the lifestyle programme had reduced their risk of getting type 2 diabetes by 58 per cent and lost 5 to 7 per cent of their body weight. Only 14 per cent had developed diabetes during the study compared to 29 per cent of those who did not take part in the lifestyle programme. Of those who took metformin, 22 per cent developed diabetes. The programme suggests that a successful diet and exercise programme is more effective at preventing diabetes than medication.

"Every year a person can live free of diabetes means an added year of life free of pain, disability, and medical costs incurred by this disease."

(Dr Allen Spiegel, director of the National Institute of Diabetes and Digestive and Kidney Diseases, USA)

Exercise combined with good diet improves general health and can prevent diabetes.

Regular testing

An essential part of treatment for people with diabetes is testing the amount of **glucose** they have in their body. This lets them know if their **blood-glucose levels** are going too high or too low.

Urine tests

Tests can be done on both **urine** and blood. Urine tests are simple to do. A specially prepared stick or strip is dipped in a sample of urine and changes colour according to the amount of glucose in the urine. However, in some people, glucose only starts to appear in their urine when the level in their blood is very high. So they may think their blood-glucose levels are fine and be unaware that they need to adapt their treatment. The other drawback of urine tests (which are not generally used by people with type 1 diabetes) is that they do not show when glucose levels are too low.

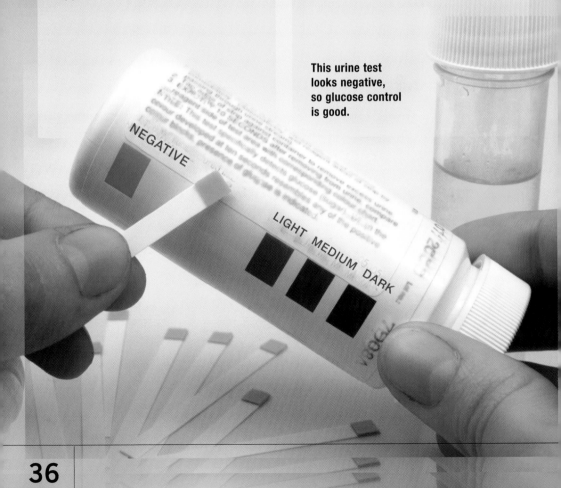

This urine test looks negative, so glucose control is good.

NEGATIVE

LIGHT MEDIUM DARK

This man is holding a glucose test strip against a scale to check his blood-glucose level.

Blood tests

Blood tests give a more accurate reading, and they show when glucose levels are too high or too low. The test can be done by pricking a finger to get a tiny sample of blood. The sample is put on to a strip and is read by a small monitor. This gives a precise measurement of the amount of glucose in the sample.

If the reading is low, the person will need to take some glucose, or have a sweet drink or something to eat, such as a sandwich or biscuit. A single high reading on its own may not be a problem, especially if a person is not feeling ill. But if the level does not return to normal within a few hours, the dose of **insulin** may need to be changed.

Regular testing

Some people test their glucose level once or twice a day, while others test more often. They need to vary the time of day that they do the test, so that they can get a complete picture of how well their glucose levels are being controlled throughout the day. Regular testing also shows how much effect food and exercise are having on a particular individual's glucose and energy levels. It is important to record the results so that the person with diabetes, or the doctor or diabetes nurse, can check trends over a period of time.

Adapting treatment to lifestyle

Oscar-winning actress Halle Berry has never let diabetes get in the way of her successful Hollywood career. Famous for her roles in *X Men*, *Monsters Ball* and *Die Another Day* Halle needs regular injections of **insulin** to treat her diabetes. As a result of her own experiences, she is actively involved with a US charity that helps children with diabetes and their families.

Halle's diabetes was discovered when she collapsed while making an ill-fated TV sitcom, *Living Dolls*, in 1989. At first she was concerned about how her co-stars would react to her illness:

'Sometimes, in the middle of a work day, it can be a little inconvenient to say: I have to go shoot up [with insulin]. Can you excuse me please? I used to think in the beginning "Oh, they're going to think I'm a prima donna." But I got over that [by] saying: "This is life." ' (*Videoflicks*, April 2000)

Nearly 15 years on, and Halle manages her diabetes around filming and her glamorous lifestyle. Like many other people with diabetes, she makes sure that her life is not ruled by strict dietary rules and regulations.

Diabetes does not stand in the way of demanding film roles for Halle Berry.

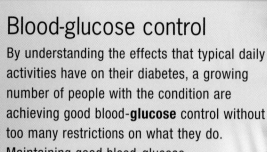

Blood-glucose control

By understanding the effects that typical daily activities have on their diabetes, a growing number of people with the condition are achieving good blood-**glucose** control without too many restrictions on what they do. Maintaining good blood-glucose control is about balancing energy intake with output, with a little help from anti-diabetic medication.

People with diabetes are encouraged to eat regular, balanced meals and take plenty of exercise. If they need to miss a meal or they know they are going to eat later than usual, they may need to reduce or delay their dose of medication. In the same way, if they know they are going to work out in the gym or take some other strenuous exercise, they will need extra energy and need to adapt their treatment.

The aim is for people to change their treatment to suit their lifestyle. They need to be sure that they are keeping good control of their **blood-glucose levels**, without risking a hypo. But they do not need to go without all the treats that other people enjoy.

Diet myths

You may have heard that people with diabetes should not eat sweets, biscuits, cakes or other 'naughty but nice' foods that many of us enjoy. That is not true. People with diabetes can eat some sugary, high-calorie foods. But, like anyone who is trying to eat a healthy, balanced diet and control their weight, they should not eat too many sweet and fatty things.

Healthy eating

Healthy eating means eating regular meals, based on starchy foods such as bread, pasta, potatoes and unsweetened breakfast cereals. Healthy eating also means eating at least five portions of fruit and vegetables each day. These not only contain vitamins, they are high in fibre, which helps digestion and **glucose** absorption.

Healthy eating means cutting back on fatty foods and those that are cooked in oil, such as burgers and chips. Vegetable fats, whether used as spreads or for cooking, are better than animal fats. Baking or grilling food cuts down on the amount of oil in a typical meal. Eating white meat and fish rather than fatty red meat also reduces fat intake.

Making sensible choices

People with diabetes are advised to choose low-calorie drinks and foods, with no added sugar, though they do not need to cut out sugar completely. Many products use low amounts of sugar or alternative sweeteners, such as fruit juice. It should not be difficult to find brands that are healthy and taste good.

Some stores sell 'diabetic' brands that are specially designed for people with diabetes. Such foods became popular in the 1960s when people with diabetes were advised to eat a sugar-free, low-carbohydrate diet. 'Diabetic' foods usually contain sweeteners such as sorbitol or fructose. These sweeteners are not classed as sugars but, in fact, they act in the same way as sugars once they are in the body.

Experts now advise people with diabetes to choose low-fat, low-sugar brands of normal foods rather than pay higher prices for 'diabetic' foods.

"Labelling confectionery and biscuits as 'suitable for diabetics' undermines advice to people with diabetes to eat a healthy diet, high in carbohydrates like cereals, pasta, rice and bread, including fruit and vegetables, but low in fat."

(Sir John Krebs, Chairman of the UK Food Standards Agency)

Living with diabetes

Sir Steve Redgrave's story

When top Olympic champion rower, Steve Redgrave, was diagnosed with type 2 diabetes, he thought his international career was over. His rowing depended on a very high level of fitness and good health. But his diabetes specialists and trainers helped him to develop a diet and treatment plan that enabled him to continue competing at the highest level. He won his fifth consecutive gold medal at the 2000 Olympic Games in Sydney, Australia.

Of his diabetes, he says: 'At first I went into a denial phase – you do not want to accept that this thing is happening to you – and took as little **insulin** as possible. But after some months, I ended up taking as much as I could, always keeping in mind the maximum permitted dose. It isn't rocket science – frankly, it's pretty straightforward. Nevertheless, the level of ignorance is amazing. That's why I'm keen to promote greater testing and to tell people that coping with diabetes is as much about controlling your lifestyle as it is about health.' (*Balance*, May/June 2001)

Steve tests his **blood-glucose levels** six or seven times a day with a small, hand-held device that fits into his briefcase. Regular testing enables him to tailor his dose of insulin to the amount of **glucose** there is in his body, and the energy he requires. Needless to say, he needs a lot more energy when he is rowing than when he is watching TV.

Continuous activity

Since winning his gold medal and receiving his knighthood, Sir Steve has taken part in an almost continuous round of sporting, educational and publicity activities. He has played golf alongside Tiger Woods and attended a birthday party for boxing legend

Muhammad Ali. But Steve has never been one to blow his own trumpet, and he believes that the best way to prove yourself is to show people your skills rather than talk about them.

'If you're the best in the world, that's good enough – it speaks for itself. So there's no reason to make more of it by mouthing off. The best way to prove your ability is by winning the race. Sport is very black and white in that way.' (*Balance*, May/June 2001)

Sir Steve Redgrave (centre) has won five Olympic gold medals despite his diabetes.

Emotional distress

Diabetes does not cause **depression**. But living with any serious, long-term condition can be distressing, and diabetes is no exception. Everyone has ups and downs in the way they feel about their diabetes, and it is quite natural to feel fed up about it from time to time.

Anxiety and depression

At least one in five people become clinically depressed at some time in their lives, whether or not they have a serious condition. Many more experience periods of feeling miserable, which can have many different triggers, such as problems at home or at school, stress at work or the break-up of a relationship.

Research has shown that anxiety and depression are more common in people with diabetes. This may be due partly to the changes in **blood-glucose levels** that they experience.

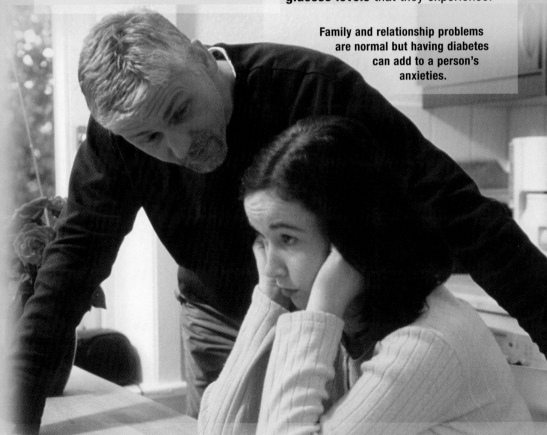

Family and relationship problems are normal but having diabetes can add to a person's anxieties.

If they are depressed, people with diabetes may neglect their blood tests, injections and diet. This can make their diabetes worse which, in turn, makes their depression worse.

Stigma

For people with diabetes, there are added factors that may make them anxious or depressed at times. They may be finding it hard to keep good control of their blood-glucose levels or they may be upset or embarrassed by having episodes of **hypoglycaemia**. Despite the fact that diabetes is so common, some people still feel that there is a stigma attached to the condition. They feel that they are somehow labelled as different, abnormal, unreliable.

Feelings of failure

If they are overweight, the need to diet and miss out on favourite foods may be depressing for people with diabetes. Having to increase the dose of drugs or add more treatments may also be depressing. It appears to indicate a worsening of the diabetes or a failure to control it effectively.

The appearance of complications of diabetes is another depressing

milestone for some people. Many people develop eye, foot or circulation problems even when they keep their **glucose** levels under reasonable control. This is distressing too.

Depression is treatable. Talking about it with a doctor, counsellor or other therapist helps people come to terms with and develop strategies for coping with the problems that are triggering the depression. When talking on its own does not seem to be helping, a course of properly prescribed anti-depressant drugs can be helpful.

❝Every time I tested my blood sugar and wasn't able to achieve the results that I was wanting to achieve – even though I was doing everything I could – my self-esteem would be knocked down another step on that ladder.❞

(Nicole Johnson, Miss America 1999, *Health Talk*, Diabetes Education Network)

Pancreatic transplants

Giving someone with diabetes a pancreatic transplant means replacing some or all of their faulty **islets of Langerhans cells** with healthy ones that will produce **insulin** for them. Until recently the operation has not been as successful as other transplant surgery, for example **kidney**, heart and liver transplants. But doctors have made important progress since the mid-1990s in transplanting islet cells from donated **pancreases** into people with severe type 1 diabetes.

The Edmonton Protocol

In 1995, researchers working in Edmonton, Canada, reported an important advance. They had extracted islet cells from donated pancreases from people who had died and injected them into the liver of people with serious type 1 diabetes. The technique – now called the Edmonton Protocol – is surprisingly simple and can be carried out under local **anaesthetic**. Using a fine needle, the cells are injected into the main **blood vessel** of the liver. After the transplant, people are usually able to go home within 24 hours.

The Canadian team chose the liver rather than the pancreas for their islet transplants because the liver is good at repairing itself and building new blood vessels and **support tissue**. Once the islet cells have been injected, new blood vessels form around them inside the liver. This makes it easy for the insulin that they produce to get into the bloodstream.

Researchers all over the world are now experimenting with the new technique. The initial Canadian results were very promising, with people getting good **glucose** control after their operation. However, researchers need to check the long-term effects of surgery over several years before they can recommend it more widely.

As the islet cells come from donated pancreases, the people receiving them need to take drugs to prevent them from rejecting the cells, which are different from their own. These anti-rejection drugs have **side effects**, so doctors use as low doses as possible.

Pig donors

A shortage of human donors has also led scientists to look elsewhere for a ready supply. In the 1980s, Swedish doctors used pig islet cells to treat diabetes in human patients, with some success. Since then, researchers have been breeding pigs that have been genetically altered to make their cells more like those of humans. This makes their organs, including their pancreatic cells, more suitable for people. There is less risk of the cells being rejected and destroyed by the human immune system, which defends the body against infection.

Can modern science cure diabetes?

Diabetes is only likely to be cured if doctors can find a way to correct the underlying mechanisms that cause the condition. For people with type 1 diabetes, that would mean preventing their immune **cells** from attacking and destroying the islet cells in their **pancreas** that make **insulin**. Alternatively, some way to help them to produce the **hormone** would need to be found.

For people with type 2 diabetes, a cure would mean preventing their cells from becoming resistant to the effects of insulin. There needs to be a way to stop their islet cells becoming exhausted by their body's increasing demands for the hormone.

Using genetic research

Finding and correcting the abnormal **genes** of people with both types of diabetes – so-called '**gene therapy**' – would be an attractive solution. However, gene therapy is proving difficult enough for conditions such as cystic fibrosis, which have only one faulty gene. Correcting the various abnormal genes linked to diabetes is way beyond the abilities of today's scientists.

Instead, scientists hope they will gain greater understanding of how immune cells destroy islet cells in type 1 diabetes. Then they may find ways to suppress their destructive activity. Identifying diabetes genes would still be useful because it would help doctors to target their treatments at those who need them most. They could check newborn babies for faulty genes for type 1 diabetes and then give these children drugs to stop the destruction of their pancreatic cells.

Uncovering the genes that make people more likely to become **obese** – and to get type 2 diabetes – will help to target treatment for this condition as well. Researchers are trying to find the body's control switches that break down in type 2 diabetes and lead to gradual failure of islet cells. They also need to work out how environmental factors, such as diet, exercise and obesity, fit into the picture.

When the puzzle is complete, they may be able to use drugs to re-programme the control switches so that people do not develop types 2 diabetes or can be treated as soon as things start to go wrong.

Can modern science cure diabetes?

Whose responsibility?

Doctors and scientists have made enormous progress in understanding diabetes. But, as the number of people around the world with diabetes moves steadily towards the 200 million mark, there is an urgent need for better treatments and for more widespread education about the dangers of becoming overweight and obese.

Many of those in developing countries hope for a more Western lifestyle, with fast foods, fast cars and easy lifestyles. But they come at a high price to health. Experts predict that, over the next 20 years, the biggest increases in diabetes will come in the developing countries of Asia, Africa and South America.

The cost of treatment

New treatments for the growing population with diabetes will be expensive. Already, millions of people in the poorer parts of the world cannot afford many important medicines, for example those needed to treat AIDS.

Genetic tests to identify people at high risk of diabetes will require expensive, high-tech equipment. The prices of new drugs to prevent islet cells being destroyed in type 1 diabetes or becoming insulin resistant in type 2 diabetes will reflect the hundreds of millions of dollars spent on their research. Islet cell transplantation

Fast food restaurants are opening up in countries such as China.

will be available only to those who can afford the surgery and the drugs that will be needed to prevent rejection of the precious new cells.

Prevention not cure

In the long term, preventing diabetes will be the best option, especially for those living in poorer countries. If health workers can find those at high risk at an early stage – when their weight and **blood-glucose levels** are just starting to rise – they can help people to change their lifestyle so that they do not develop full-scale type 2 diabetes.

This type of **screening** and education programme requires time and money from healthcare providers. Also, people at risk of diabetes need to decide to change their lifestyle. But if people do agree to take charge of their health, they may be able to avoid a lifetime of medical treatment. They can prevent serious eye, **kidney**, nerve and heart diseases that could limit their everyday activities and shorten their lives.

❝Governments can and must contribute to the battle ... by encouraging and facilitating lifestyle changes, providing health education for all and investing in primary prevention programmes. There can be no doubt that now is the time to act.❞

(Professor George Alberti, President of the International Diabetes Federation, 2002)

Information and advice

There are many organizations that can offer advice and information about living with diabetes. Some can offer a counselling service to provide support for people with the condition. There are diabetes organizations that also undertake research into finding a cure for diabetes.

Contacts in the UK

Diabetes UK
10 Parkway
London NW1 7AA
Careline: 020 7424 1030 (Monday–Friday 9 a.m.–5 p.m.)
Textphone: 020 7424 1888
Email: careline@diabetes.org.uk
Website: www.diabetes.org.uk
Campaigns on behalf of people with diabetes, provides support and information, and funds research. The Careline has trained counsellors who can be contacted for support and current information on diabetes, although they cannot give personal medical advice. The Careline also operates an email enquiry service.

Diabetes Research & Wellness Foundation
Office 101–102
Northney Marina
Hayling Island
Hampshire PO11 0NH
Tel: 023 9263 7808
Email: drwf@diabeteswellnessnet.org.uk
Website: www.diabeteswellnessnet.org.uk
An organization that funds research and offers support to people living with diabetes.

Contacts in the USA

American Diabetes Association
ATTN: National Call Center
1701 North Beauregard Street
Alexandria, VA 22311
Tel: 1-800-DIABETES (1-800-342-2383).
Website: www.diabetes.org
A national organization providing information and support to people with diabetes and their families, health professionals and others who want to know more about the condition.

Contacts in Australia

Diabetes Australia
1st Floor, Churchill House
218 Northbourne Ave
Braddon ACT 2612
Website: www.diabetesaustralia.com.au
Part of a federation of twelve medical, educational and scientific, research and community-based organizations, including the Australian Diabetes Society, the Australian Diabetes Educators Association, the Kellion Diabetes Foundation and the Diabetes Research Foundation-Western Australia.

Contacts in New Zealand

Diabetes New Zealand
Freepost DNZ
PO Box 54
Oamaru
Tel: 0800 342 238
Website: www.diabetes.org.nz
Offers support for people with diabetes across the country.

Websites

Children with Diabetes
www.childrenwithdiabetes.com/
index_cwd.htm
A US-based site geared towards promoting understanding of the care and treatment of diabetes, especially in children.

Diabetes Insight
www.diabetic.org.uk
UK website aiming to provide information to people with diabetes in a positive manner to help them live an active life. Operates an email support group and an online discussion forum, Diabetes Support.

The Diabetes Monitor
www.diabetesmonitor.com
Extensive collection of resources and other websites related to diabetes

Further reading

American Diabetes Association Complete Guide to Diabetes, by American Diabetes Association (Editor); McGraw-Hill, 2002. Advice and information on diabetes from the leading US diabetes charity.

Living with Diabetes, by Jenny Bryan; Hodder Wayland, 1998. Advice on how to manage diabetes and information on the equipment needed and people who can help.

Living with Diabetes: the Diabetes UK Guide for Those Treated with Diet & Tablets, by J. L. Day; John Wiley, 2001. Advice and information mainly on type 2 diabetes from the leading diabetes charity in the UK.

Living with Diabetes: the Diabetes UK Guide for Those Treated with Insulin, by J. L. Day; John Wiley, 2002. Advice and information mainly on type 1 diabetes from the leading diabetes charity in the UK.

Mr Food's Every Day's a Holiday Diabetic Cookbook, by Art Ginsbury and Nicole Johnson; American Diabetes Association, 2002. Useful recipes for people with diabetes.

One Pot Meals for People with Diabetes, by Ruth Glick and Nancy Baggett; American Diabetes Association, 2002. Simple meals for people with diabetes.

The Uncomplicated Guide to Diabetes Complications, 2nd Edition by Marvin E. Levin, MD & Michael A. Pfeifer, MD, MS, CDE, FACE (Editors); American Diabetes Asssociation, 2002. A guide to treating and preventing the complications of diabetes.

What to Do When You Have Type 2 Diabetes (Fast Facts), by Janice Betz; American Diabetes Association, 2002. Advice and information on type 2 diabetes from the leading diabetes charity in the USA.

Glossary

abdomen
lower part of the body, extending from the chest to the pelvis; it contains all the digestive organs, such as the stomach, intestines, liver and pancreas

amputate
cut off a part of the body, such as a limb, in a surgical operation

anaesthetic
a drug that makes a person unable to feel anything, especially pain, in a part of the body or the whole body

anatomist
an expert in the structure of the human body

bacteria
microbes that can cause infection

blood-glucose level
the amount of glucose in the blood

blood vessels
small hollow tubes, including arteries, veins and capillaries, that carry blood around the body

carbohydrates
chemical compounds that contain carbon, hydrogen and oxygen. Carbohydrates are the main source of energy for animals.

cell
smallest unit of living things, including parts of the human body, such as the pancreas

depression
feelings of extreme sadness, hopelessness, lack of energy, and feeling 'outside' of normal life

dialysis
technique to purify the blood for those whose kidneys do not work: their blood is passed through a large machine that removes toxic substances

digestive enzymes
proteins that the digestive system uses to break down food so that nutrients can be absorbed into the bloodstream

enzyme
a substance that helps a biological change happen or happen more quickly, without being changed itself

epidemic
a disease that affects a large number of people and spreads rapidly

ethnic group
a group of people who share a common culture, tradition and sometimes language

gene
a unit inside a cell that controls a particular quality in a living thing that has been passed on from its parents

gene therapy
technique to change a gene, to correct a faulty gene or replace a missing gene

genetic engineering
the science of changing how a living thing develops by changing the information in its genes

gland
a small part of the body that produces chemicals, such as insulin

glucose
type of sugar widely used in animal cells to provide energy

hormone
a substance produced in the body that influences how the cells and tissues function

hypoglycaemia
abnormally low levels of glucose in the bloodstream

insulin
hormone that enables glucose to move from the bloodstream into cells

insulin resistance
condition in which cells no longer respond to insulin

islets of Langerhans
the cells in the pancreas that produce insulin, which controls glucose levels in the body

kidneys
organs in the abdomen that control urine production and blood pressure

metformin
drug that is used in the treatment of type 2 diabetes

microbe
an extremely small living thing that may cause disease

nerves
long, thin thread-like structures that carry messages between the brain and parts of the body, allowing you to move, feel pain and other sensations

obese
so overweight that the person's health is at risk

pancreas
an organ near the stomach that produces insulin and enzymes that help the body to digest food

protein
important part of food which is needed for growth and to repair damaged parts of the body

reservations
an area of land in the USA that is kept separate for Native Americans to live on. Not all Native Americans live on reservations.

screening
method of finding out whether a group of people have a disease or condition by asking them to go to a clinic for one or more tests

side effects
changes caused by a drug which are not the intended effects, and which may be harmful

sulphonylureas
drugs that are used to treat type 2 diabetes by increasing insulin production by the pancreas

support tissue
the tissue that surrounds nerves and protects them from damage

urine
fluid produced by the kidneys, which contains the body's waste products

Index